- These student worksheets are intended to act alongside the corre   help reinforce your understanding and improve your confidence.

- Every worksheet is cross-referenced to *GCSE Design and Technology*   r

- The questions concentrate purely on the content you need to cover, and the limited space forces you to choose your answer carefully.

These worksheets can be used ...

... as <u>classwork sheets</u> where pupils use their revision guide to provide the answers ...

... as <u>harder classwork sheets</u> where pupils study the topic first, then answer the questions without their guides ...

... as easy to mark <u>homework sheets</u> which test understanding and reinforce learning ...

... as the basis for <u>learning homeworks</u> which are then tested in subsequent lessons ...

... as <u>test material</u> for topics or entire modules ...

... as <u>a structured revision programme</u> prior to the exams.

- Remember to fill in your score at the bottom of each page in the small grey box  , and also to put your score in the 'marks' column on the contents page.

- This workbook, and the companion revision guide, have been checked against the examboard specifications for examination in 2007 onwards. Where necessary the content has been revised and supplemented to ensure it remains relevant and reliable.

Score   Page No.

Introduction

Fibres and Fabrics

Colour and Decoration

The Design Process

©Lonsa

Score   Page No.

The Design Process (cont)

The Manufacturing Industry

Other Issues

1. Ask your teacher for the following information:

a) The name of your Awarding Body.

b) The deadline for your coursework.

c) The date of your mock exam.

d) The date of the Year II final exam.

2. a) What percentage does your coursework contribute to your final mark?

b) What percentage is your written examination paper worth?

3. What should your completed coursework folder consist of?

4. In your coursework, you need to show a good understanding of...

i) M _ _ _ _ _ I _ _ _ _

ii) T _ _ _ _ _ _ Q _ _ _ _

iii) C _ M _ _ _ _ _ _ _ _

iv) I _ D _ _ _ _ _ _ _ _ P _ _ _ _ _ _ _ _ _

v) P _ _ _ _ _ _ _ _ S

5. a) List six of the areas you will need to look at to help you present, develop and manufacture your own ideas effectively.

i)

ii)

iii)

iv)

v)

vi)

b) Name four different techniques you will need to explore.

i)

ii)

iii)

iv)

1. What four things do we need textiles for?

i)

ii)

iii)

iv)

2. What does the term 'Textiles' mean? Write your own short definition.

3. Name six kinds of textile products and find examples in magazines and catalogues to illustrate each of your answers.

i)

Examples

ii)

Examples

iii)

Examples

iv)

Examples

v)

Examples

vi)

Examples

List six industries in which textiles have advanced uses.

i)

ii)

iii)

iv)

v)

vi)

1. Complete the following passage.

Textiles Technology involves the use of specialist [_____] and [_____]

which have specific [_____] that allow you to do particular jobs correctly and

effectively. You must [_____] equipment and tools that are [_____]

for the work you want to carry out. You need to be able to [_____] what they look li[...]

and how they work. You should also be able to use them [_____] , [_____]

and efficiently.

2. a) What are the five main areas that tools and equipment can be divided into?

i) _____   ii) _____

iii) _____   iv) _____

v) _____

b) What is a 'Component'?

3. a) Batik pots are an example of specialist design equipment. Describe what they are used for.

b) What is a 'squeegee' used for in screen printing?

c) How do you 'set' designs created with fabric crayons and pens to stop them washing off?

4. Name one example of a piece of pressing equipment and one way in which it can be used.

Example: [_____]   Function: [_____]

1. Name three examples of machine based sewing and joining equipment and three examples of non-machine based sewing and joining equipment.

MACHINE BASED

i) _____

ii) _____

iii) _____

NON-MACHINE BASED

i) _____

ii) _____

iii) _____

2. Identify two pieces of sewing and joining equipment (machine and/or non-machine based) that you would use to complete the following tasks.

a) Embroider a motif onto the breast pocket of a jacket.

i) _____   ii) _____

b) Join together two pieces of material to make a soft toy.

i) _____   ii) _____

c) Prepare the sections of material needed to make a skirt using a paper pattern.

i) _____   ii) _____

3. a) What is the main difference between a standard sewing machine and a computerised sewing machine?

b) Give two other pieces of sewing and joining equipment that can be used in conjunction with a computer.

i) _____   ii) _____

4. Why must great care be taken when working with machine based equipment?

5. Describe one way in which advanced equipment is used in Textiles Technology.

1.   Identify the different components to complete the crossword below.

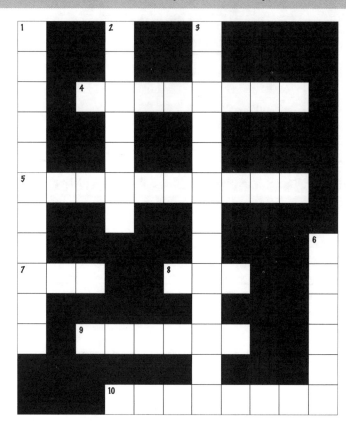

ACROSS

4.   Often described as 'narrow fabrics'. (8)
5.   Buttons, press-studs and zips are all example of these. (10)
7.   Normally used to draw onto fabric. (3)
8.   Used to apply colour to fabric. (3)
9.   Also called 'hook and loop fastening.' (6)
10. Stretchy, flexible components with many uses. (8)

DOWN

1.   Used to reinforce fabrics. (11)
2.   These can vary for 1 down and 3 down. (7)
3.   Available for hand and machine use. (8,5)
6.   Specialist varieties are available for material like silk. (6)

2.   Make lists of the tools and equipment you might need to complete one of the following tasks.

a) Produce an overnight bag with a shoulder strap and inside pocket to keep valuables safe.
b) Make a pair of removable cushion covers with matching designs embroidered on the front.
c) Make a short-sleeved work shirt with a collar.

Task ☐ (specify a), b) or c))

MACHINE EQUIPMENT	MATERIALS

NON-MACHINE EQUIPMENT	COMPONENTS

1. a) What is the difference between staple fibres and filament fibres?

b) What must happen to fibres before they are used to make fabrics?

2. For each of the fibres listed below, tick the appropriate column to indicate whether they are NATURAL, SYNTHETIC or REGENERATED

	NATURAL	SYNTHETIC	REGENERATED
Polyvinyl chloride (PVC)			
Lyocell			
Ramie			
Alpaca			
Polyester			
Modal			
Cotton			
Acrylic			
Mohair			
Wool			
Elastomeric			
Acetate			
Viscose			
Silk			
Polyethylene			
Linen			

3. a) Describe the origin of synthetic fibres.

b) Describe the origin of regenerated fibres.

4. a) What are yarns?

b) What is the difference between S twist and Z twist?

c) What is the difference between yarns produced using the Worsted and Woollen Spinning Systems?

1. For each of the fabrics listed below tick the appropriate column to indicate whether they are WOVEN, KNITTED or FELTED/BONDED.

	WOVEN	KNITTED	FELTED/BONDED
Terry towelling			
Carpet underlay			
Car seat coverings			
Corduroy			
Denim			
Velour			
Damask			
Hats			
Calico			
Single jersey T-shirts			
Jacquard			
Lace			
Double jersey T-shirts			
Nets			
Cloths			

2. Write down the names of the natural or synthetic fibres whose key manufacturing processes are listed below:

a) Cellulose sheets are dissolved in organic solvent to form a solution, which is then extruded and hardened off in a process called wet spinning.

b) Grading is followed by scouring and carbonising before carding and combing straightens the fabric. Finally spinning occurs.

c) Wood pulp is treated with acetic acid and then follows a process similar to a) above. Fibres are eventually extruded into a stream of warm air. This is known as dry spinning.

d) Harvesting is followed by drying and ginning before carding and combing straightens the fibres. The slivers are then drawn into roving before spinning occurs.

e) Chemicals derived from oil are polymerised. The polymer produced is melted and extruded in a process known as melt spinning.

f) Cocoons of this particular moth are harvested and heated in order to remove the gum holding the cocoon together. Yarn is then produced by spinning.

1. a) **What type of knitting is shown in the diagram alongside?**

    b) **In which direction do the interlocking loops run?**

    c) **Give an example of a type of fabric produced by this particular method of knitting.**

2. a) **What type of knitting is shown in the diagram alongside?**

    b) **In which direction do the interlocking loops run?**

    c) **Give an example of a type of fabric produced by this particular method of knitting.**

3. a) **Describe one advantage the type of knitting in question 2 has over that in question 1.**

    b) **Describe one disadvantage of either of these two methods.**

4. **For each of the statements below, circle the appropriate word to indicate whether it is true or false.**

    a) Knitted fabrics are made in the same way as woven fabrics.   TRUE/FALSE

    b) Knitted fabrics consist of interlocking loops.   TRUE/FALSE

    c) Knitted fabrics aren't stretchy.   TRUE/FALSE

    d) They can be made even less stretchy by adding Elastane.   TRUE/FALSE

    e) Knitted fabrics can be bulked up by napping.   TRUE/FALSE

    f) Knitted fabrics can help to keep you cool.   TRUE/FALSE

    g) Elastane can be added to increase extension.   TRUE/FALSE

    h) Weft knits are 'stretchier' than warp knits.   TRUE/FALSE

    i) Brushing produces a fluffy surface in knitted fabrics.   TRUE/FALSE

    j) Only natural fibres can be used in knitting.   TRUE/FALSE

1. In the spaces provided on the diagram, label the Warp and the Weft

a) _____

b)

c) How does this compare with the direction of the rows in warp knitting and weft knitting?

d) What name is given to the type of machine that produces fabric like this?

2. Name each of the various weaves being described below:

a) Made on a special loom controlled by a computer. This type of fabric is expensive and high quality.

b) Weft yarns pass over and under either 2 or 4 warp yarns creating a diagonal pattern.

c) Has a pile made of loops (e.g. towelling) or thread (e.g. corduroy).

3. Describe the main differences between Plain weave and Satin weave.

4. For each of the statements below, circle the appropriate word to indicate whether it is true or false.

a) Woven fabrics are made in the same way as knitted fabrics. TRUE/FALSE
b) Woven fabrics consist of interlocking loops. TRUE/FALSE
c) Woven fabrics aren't particularly stretchy. TRUE/FALSE
d) They can be made even less stretchy by adding Elastane. TRUE/FALSE
e) Elastane can be added to increase extension. TRUE/FALSE
f) Only natural fibres can be used in weaving. TRUE/FALSE
g) Woven fabrics fray easily when cut. TRUE/FALSE
h) They are stronger along the straight grain of the fabric. TRUE/FALSE
i) A close weave is stronger than a loose weave. TRUE/FALSE
j) Woven fabrics are more fire resistant than knitted fabrics. TRUE/FALSE

1.   a) How do non-woven fabrics differ from woven or knitted fabrics?

b) Give three examples of products which utilise non-woven fabrics.

i)   ii)   iii)

2.   a) Describe how wool felts are produced.

b) Describe how needle felts are produced.

c) Describe how bonded fabrics are produced.

3.   Describe one example of how another non-woven fabric is used.

4.   For each of the statements below, circle the appropriate word to indicate whether it is true or false.

a) Non-woven fabrics are made in the same way as knitted fabrics.   TRUE/FALSE
b) Bonded fabrics don't fray easily.   TRUE/FALSE
c) Non-woven fabrics consist of interlocking loops.   TRUE/FALSE
d) Non-woven fabrics have no grain and aren't stretchy.   TRUE/FALSE
e) Non-woven fabrics are weaker than knitted and woven fabrics.   TRUE/FALSE
f) Non-woven fabrics are impermeable.   TRUE/FALSE
g) Non-woven fabrics can only be made from natural fibres.   TRUE/FALSE
h) Hats are often made from non-woven fabrics.   TRUE/FALSE
i) Wool felts are more fire resistant that knitted fabrics.   TRUE/FALSE
j) Adhesives are never used in bonded fabrics.   TRUE/FALSE

1. The word search below contains words which describe the properties of polyester and cotton. Identify these words by drawing a line through them. (There are 10 properties.)

Q	D	G	Y	Y	T	I	C	I	T	S	A	L	E	H	G	I	H
S	E	B	F	B	J	D	C	A	N	G	T	S	I	F	I	B	E
F	E	E	G	V	K	U	G	H	J	I	O	S	F	I	E	S	T
E	R	W	V	E	R	Y	S	T	R	O	N	G	O	K	F	B	Y
F	J	V	Y	R	E	S	T	A	Y	B	E	P	O	L	V	E	Y
E	V	E	R	Y	C	H	E	A	P	E	B	J	S	R	E	I	P
N	G	O	U	D	L	J	P	W	E	E	T	R	Y	D	F	G	K
O	Q	U	W	U	Z	C	V	H	Y	R	J	L	S	F	G	U	O
I	T	Y	C	R	E	A	S	E	R	E	S	I	S	T	A	N	T
T	E	W	H	A	E	S	F	G	H	L	J	R	R	F	Y	O	O
A	Q	P	N	B	A	F	J	D	G	J	O	W	T	U	W	T	E
L	J	P	A	L	Y	K	L	Q	D	F	V	Y	J	K	A	V	J
U	B	A	D	E	W	C	O	D	E	F	H	A	C	F	D	E	B
S	Q	G	F	L	G	S	A	R	J	F	H	A	S	D	G	R	L
N	G	D	O	D	H	K	A	B	S	O	R	B	E	N	T	Y	G
I	E	V	J	K	D	C	K	E	H	A	S	D	V	I	O	E	D
D	D	G	H	L	O	O	B	C	E	A	D	S	B	K	S	L	I
O	X	S	D	T	D	O	N	H	K	S	W	C	I	D	G	A	L
O	G	S	Y	S	F	L	L	W	B	R	E	R	B	T	E	S	P
G	D	S	O	G	D	I	B	G	B	C	S	D	F	G	N	T	M
G	A	H	S	C	V	N	M	D	V	E	R	T	L	S	E	I	N
E	E	A	S	F	F	G	E	E	S	B	M	L	E	V	J	C	X

2. Place the properties you have found into the table below. A property may be placed in both columns if appropriate.

PROPERTIES OF POLYESTER	PROPERTIES OF COTTON

1. Identify the fabrics which are loosely described below:

a) I am extracted from wood pulp and am resistant to biological breakdown. Although I don't get more than 2 stars for any particular property, I am very versatile.

My name is

b) I am a natural product and fairly expensive. I am both cooling and absorbent.

My name is

c) I originate from oil and score low on absorbency. I am strong and crease resistant and often used in carpets.

My name is

d) I am a natural product which is soft and hard wearing. For warmth, I am superb.

My name is

e) I am synthetic, sporty and durable. When stretched I simply spring back to my original shape.

My name is

f) I am produced naturally from plant material and am cheap, strong and cooling. I crease easily.

My name is

g) I am a good all round synthetic and often blended with other fibres. I am not very absorbent.

My name is

h) I am natural, cooling and absorbent but sadly I crease easily. I am stronger when wet.

My name is

i) I am extracted from wood pulp and referred to as synthetic silk. I am light and absorbent.

My name is

2. Apart from the properties listed on p17 of the revision guide, name 4 others which you think might be important in describing a fabric.

i)

ii)

iii)

iv)

1. a) Why do manufacturers often use fibres, yarns or fabrics that have been enhanced or have certain built-in qualities?

b) Name four textile products that make use of fibres, yarns or fabrics of this type.

i)

ii)

iii)

iv)

2. Complete the crossword on 'fibres and fabrics with special properties' using the clues below.

ACROSS
1. A high stretch fibre. (8)
5. A material which is five times stronger than steel. (6)
6. A type of fabric which allows air in but keeps moisture out. (7)
7. Fibres finer than human hair made from polyamide or polyester. (11)
8. The manufacturers of 2 down. (6)
9. The type of membrane used in sympatex. (11)

DOWN
2. An example (perhaps the best known) of a high stretch fibre. (5)
3. Developed for use by fire fighters. (5)
4. A property of some vests made from Kevlar. (6,8)

Revision Guide Reference: Page 1

1. **a) Why do textiles products have finishes applied to them?**

b) When can finishes be applied to a product?

2. **a) Give an example of how Teflon can be used as a finish.**

b) What is Purista?

c) What is Chitosan?

a) Unscramble the letters below to reveal 6 different types of finish:

SHRUBING

CRANDLEGINE

NIGNIMTALA

GNISOBSME

NOTSGNIIBO

SLIHNGIPOOBI

b) Select three of the finishing processes above and explain how the finish is applied.

i)

ii)

iii)

1. Complete the table below on chemical finishes:

Name Of Finish	Fabrics It Can Be Applied To	How It Is Done	Possible Application
Flame proofing		Chemicals are applied either at yarn or fabric stage. The aim of this finish is to slow down the burning process.	Interior fabrics, furnishings
	All fabrics	A silicone-based finish is applied, which stops the absorption of stains or dirt.	Clothing, Interior products
Anti-static			Underwear, carpets
	Cotton	The fabric is placed in a sodium hydroxide solution, which makes the fibres swell. This makes the cotton more shiny, absorbent and stronger.	Clothing
Waterproofing or water repelling	All fabrics		Clothing, tents
Crease resistance			Clothing
	Wool	A resin based finish can be applied, or a chemical treatment with chlorine can be used. Products labelled machine washable or superwash have this finish applied.	Clothing
Anti-felting		The fabric can have an oxidative finishing treatment applied to soften the scaly fibres of the wool, or it can be coated with a synthetic polymer film. This retains the warmth of wool but prevents felting.	Clothing
Bleaching			Clothing, bedding

1. Describe briefly the following finishes and give one example of their possible use.

Type Of Finish

Ultra-violet Protection	
Fire Retardant Qualities	
Fire Resistance	
Cut, Tear, Ballistic Resistance	
Abrasion Resistance	
Weatherproofing	
Thermal Insulation	
Chemical Protection	
Buoyancy	
Reflective Qualities	
Micro Encapsulation	
Antibacterial	

1. The army ask a manufacturer to develop a technical textile for them. They need a light weight mesh fabric that can support very heavy weights. Number the following qualities 1-3 in order of importance when developing this technical textile, where 1 is the most important.

a) Colour [ ]   b) Feel [ ]   c) Strength [ ]

2. Place a tick alongside the description that is most accurate.

Smart textiles can think for themselves. [ ]   Smart textiles always contain computer technology. [ ]   Smart textiles can respond to external stimuli. [ ]

3. Unscramble the words below two find four groups of smart textiles.

a) FOST FEASTNICER [ ]   b) MOUNTAINCOMIC [ ]

c) WEPRO SADSITES [ ]   d) ACIDELM [ ]

4. Carbon and steel fibres can be used to incorporate electrical circuitry into textiles to create wearable technology.

a) Name one other metal fibre that can be used for this purpose. [ ]

b) What property do these metals fibres all share, which allows them to be used to create electrical circuitry? [ ]

5. Name the three different types of energy that can be used to provide a power source in power assisted textiles.

a) [ ]   b) [ ]   c) [ ]

6. What is microencapsulation?

7. Use the Internet to find a textiles product (other than the LifeShirt®) that incorporates electronic sensors. Briefly describe the product and its function below.

1. What is a primary colour?

2. Are the following statements true or false ? (Circle your answer)

    i) Red, yellow and blue are the only primary colours.   TRUE/FALSE

    ii) Primary colours are created by mixing two colours.   TRUE/FALSE

    iii) Two primary colours give a secondary colour.   TRUE/FALSE

    iv) Green is made by mixing yellow and blue.   TRUE/FALSE

    v) Red is made by mixing purple and yellow.   TRUE/FALSE

    vi) Tertiary colours are produced by mixing a primary and secondary colour.   TRUE/FALSE

3   a) What colour is used to darken the tone?

    b) What colour is used to lighten the tone?

4. Complete the hue diagrams using the colours indicated.

    Blue Hue   Green Hue   Orange Hue

5. a) Put a circle around the combination that is an example of complementary colours.

    i) red and orange   ii) blue and orange   iii) green and blue

    b) Put a circle around the combination that is an example of harmonious colours.

    i) green and red   ii) yellow and purple   iii) yellow and green

    Name three factors that you need to consider when deciding on the colours for a product.

    i)

    ii)

    iii)

1. Name three factors that will affect the colours, pattern and textures chosen when designing a textiles product.

i) ....

ii) ....

iii) ....

2. Which of these patterns is...

a) ... REGULAR? ☐

b) ... IRREGULAR? ☐

3. Put a ring around the option that could help to achieve the aims set out in each of these briefs.

a) A dress, suitable for office wear, that helps to make the wearer look tall and slim.

i) Horizontal lines 　　　　ii) Vertical lines 　　　　iii) Checks

b) Soft furnishings for a large hotel lobby, to create a cosy, intimate atmosphere.

i) Deep red 　　　　ii) Pale blue 　　　　iii) Black and white

c) Coordinating bed linen for a family home.

i) Corduroy 　　　　ii) Velvet 　　　　iii) Brushed cotton

4. a) What would be the main influences on STYLE, if you were asked to design a garment for a high street store?

_____

b) What do designers mean by 'silhouette'?

_____

5. Ted Smith produces a scale drawing of a pair of trousers for his autumn collection. He uses a scale of 1:10 If the leg length in the drawing is 9cm, what will the leg length of the actual trousers be?

☐

1. Why is it important that the printing methods used in the textiles industry can cope with rapid development?

2. Draw a line joining each printing method to the correct description.

| Block Printing | The design is transferred from special paper onto the fabric using heated rollers. |

| Digital Printing | Dye is forced through a nylon screen onto the fabric below using a squeegee. |

| Screen Printing | A computer is used for the entire design and printing process. |

| Heat Transfer Printing | Colour is transferred onto the fabric from a block that has a design cut into it in relief. |

a) Why does Engraved Roller Printing require a series of rollers and not just one?

b) What would happen if you made the circumference of the rollers larger?

a) Are the following statements true or false?

i) Heat transfer printing can be used to create designs on any fabric. TRUE/FALSE

ii) The basic principles of heat transfer printing and computer transfer printing are the same. TRUE/FALSE

iii) Block printing is only suitable for fabrics made from natural fibres. TRUE/FALSE

iv) Digital printing is a quick and easy way to create fabric samples and one-off designs. TRUE/FALSE

v) Engraved roller printing is ideal for the mass production of printed fabrics. TRUE/FALSE

vi) It is more expensive to produce a two-colour design using screen printing methods than a five-colour design. TRUE/FALSE

b) Explain your answer to part vi) above.

1. When applying colour to fabrics, what is the main difference between printing and dyeing methods?

2. What four factors will affect the final colour of a dyed textiles product?

i)

ii)

iii)

iv)

3. Unscramble the letters to find four different dyeing methods.

i) PEERSIDS

ii) TRECID

iii) LETBAGEEV

iv) PETMING

4. a) What is a 'mordant'?

b) What does a 'resist' do?

5. Choose one method of resist dyeing and explain briefly how it works.

6. Carla buys a packet of black dye. She uses it to dye a dress and a T-shirt. The original colour of both garments is cream. The T-shirt comes out black, but the dress comes our brown. Suggest why this migh

1. From the description given, identify the method of surface decoration used in the creation of each of these products.

a) An evening gown with glass beads and sequins stitched to the bodice for an ornate finish.

b) An oven glove with a layer of protective wadding, finished with diagonal lines of stitching that produce a raised diamond effect.

c) A shoulder bag made from pieces of different coloured denim stitched together.

2. Number the following actions 1 to 8 according to the order in which they need to take place when using computer software to create an embroidery design. The first one has been done for you.

Set design parameters, stitch size, etc.

Send design to sewing machine to be produced

1 Select image

Send to printer to print design and settings

Import image into design software

Save design

Apply machine stitches

Digitize image

Name four common stitches used in hand embroidery.

i)

ii)

iii)

iv)

a) Why does the fabric manipulation technique Shibori work best with synthetic fabrics?

b) How might you strengthen pattern pieces cut from a flimsy fabric for an appliqué design?

1. Which temporary method of joining fabric together is best suited to...

a) holding several layers of fabric in place before machine sewing?

b) holding two pieces of fabric together before machine sewing a seam?

2. List four factors that will help to determine which type of seam you use to join two pieces of fabric.

a)

b)

c)

d)

3. Which type of seam would you use in the following instances?

a) To produce a neat, strong seam on a satin bra.

b) To produce a strong, flat seam on the inside leg of a pair of jeans.

c) To join and neaten the side seam of a t-shirt.

4. a) Give one disadvantage of using a plain seam.

b) Give one advantage of using a plain seam.

5. Hand stitches are generally not as secure as machine stitches. Suggest one situation in which you might choose to use hand stitches instead of machine stitches.

6. Name two types of machine stitch suitable for use on jersey (knitted) fabrics.

a)

b)

7. Pinking shears can be used to finish a plain seam and prevent the fabric from fraying. Name two other methods that can be used to finish plain seams.

a)

b)

1. Complete the flow chart below, showing each stage in the design process.

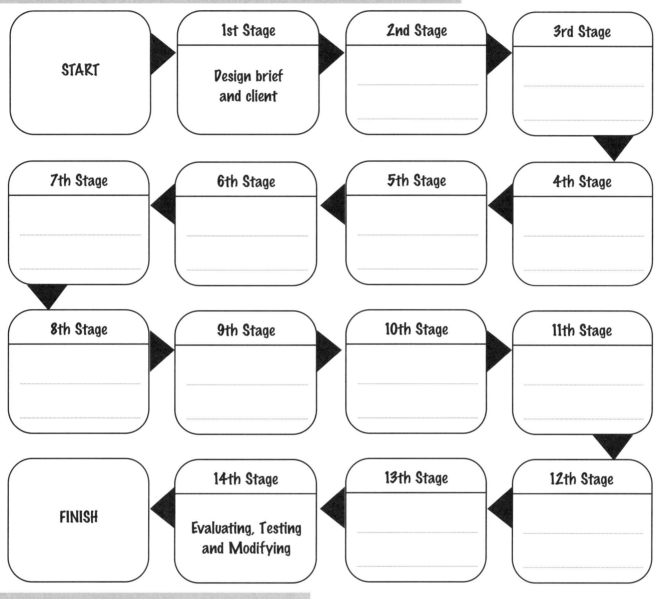

START

1st Stage

Design brief and client

2nd Stage

3rd Stage

7th Stage

6th Stage

5th Stage

4th Stage

8th Stage

9th Stage

10th Stage

11th Stage

FINISH

14th Stage

Evaluating, Testing and Modifying

13th Stage

12th Stage

. At what stage in the design process should you...

a) Identify the health and safety issues relevant to your work?   STAGE:

d) Put together costings, if necessary?   STAGE:

b) Create a Gantt Chart?   STAGE:

e) Create a mood board?   STAGE:

c) Pinpoint all the essential and desirable criteria for your product?   STAGE:

f) Find out about consumer needs and preferences?   STAGE:

When is it appropriate to give a client feedback?

1. What is the purpose of a design brief?

2. Which of these two design briefs is a closed brief and which is an open brief?

Design a range of men's long-sleeved tops for a winter sports clothing company.
Deadline: 15th August

Valentines Day Lingerie
• Matching bra and briefs
• 20-30 year age group
• Fun and contemporary
• No love hearts, cupids etc.
Deadline: January 5th

3. Complete the brainstorming diagram to show how you would start to develop one of the briefs shown above

4. Put a tick or a cross alongside each of the sentences to show if you agree or disagree.

In the Textiles Industry, at the design brief stage it is good practice to...

a) ... meet with the client to discuss the brief.

b) ... test a range of materials.

c) ... produce sketches of initial ideas.

d) ... assign jobs to different members of the design team.

e) ... produce a Gantt chart.

1. There are six key things that the process of task analysis should help you to identify. What are they?

i) _____ ii) _____

iii) _____ iv) _____

v) _____ vi) _____

2. Name three different methods you could use to present your task analysis.

i) _____ ii) _____ iii) _____

3. Look at the brief below and identify six tasks you would need to complete before you could begin working on your designs.

TASK 1

TASK 2

TASK 3

Design a costume for a male performer in a theatre production about gangsters set in 1920s America.

TASK 4

TASK 5

TASK 6

Answer true or false to the following statements.

In the textiles industry, by the end of the task analysis stage a designer expects to know...

i) ... who the products are aimed at.   TRUE/FALSE
ii) ... exactly what the final product will look like.   TRUE/FALSE
iii) ... what market research needs to be carried out.   TRUE/FALSE
iv) ... what the range/product needs to include.   TRUE/FALSE
v) ... what colour the product will be.   TRUE/FALSE

1. Why do designers analyse, test and evaluate existing products? Give two reasons.

i) ....

ii) ....

2. Choose a textiles product to analyse. Draw a sketch of it and answer the following:

e.g.

Toys and games

Interior Products
eg curtains, bedding

Indoor and
Outdoor Clothing

Other Clothing
eg. underwear, socks

Accessories
eg. hats, bags,
gloves, shoes

Sketch your product here

a) What material(s) is the product made from?

b) How have the materials been joined together? e.g. machine stitching, adhesive.

c) What method of colour application has been used?

d) What components have been used to make the product?

e) What are the care instructions for the product?

f) What is the key function of the product?

g) How would you improve this product?

1. Researching a project can produce large amounts of material, brochures and data. Underline one of the following statements which would improve your grade.

i) Include all information you have gathered.

ii) Include all information you have gathered but highlight relevant details.

iii) Include only relevant material.

iv) Include only relevant material with notes and conclusions.

2. What is the difference between PRIMARY sources and SECONDARY sources?

a) Sort the following sources of information into two groups: primary and secondary.

PRIMARY		SECONDARY
	Disassembly	
	Statistics	
	Exhibitions	
	Surveys	
	Web sites	
	Questionnaires	
	Magazines	
b) Add one extra example of your own to this list.	Books	**c)** Add one extra example of your own to this list.

Fill in the gaps to complete these sentences about important things to remember when conducting primary research.

i) In a questionnaire, questions need to be [   ] , [   ] and [   ] .

ii) When you conduct a survey, always choose a suitable [   ] .

iii) A shop report is a collection of images showing the [   ] [   ] .

iv) For an interview, always [   ] your questions and [   ] the answers.

1. Describe TWO methods of recording the responses from an interview.

i)

ii)

2. Look at the data below, which was collected in a survey, and analyse the results.

Favourite Colour Combination	Blue/Yellow	Blue/Green	Red/Green	Red/Orange
Number of Children	7 boys, 10 girls	12 boys, 6 girls	6 boys, 3 girls	5 boys, 1 girl

i) What is the total number of children in the survey?

ii) What percentage are boys?

iii) What is the most popular colour combination?

iv) If an equal number of boys and girls had taken part in the survey, which colour combination would you expect to be most popular? Explain your choice.

3. a) How could travel provide inspiration for your designs?

b) Name four other potential sources of inspiration.

i)   ii)

iii)   iv)

4. Underline the sentence which best describes 'Intelligence Gathering'.

a) The process of collecting as much general information about the textiles industry as possible to impre your client.

b) A rigorous interrogative process which allows you to make exact predictions about future trends.

c) Observing a target group and interacting with them in order to understand what might influence th choices they make as a consumer.

1. Make a check list of everything you need to include in your research analysis and evaluation.
    One has been done for you.

    i) ....

    ii) ....

    iii) ....

    iv) ....

    v) How the research gathered will help me with my work.

    vi) ....

    vii) ....

2. The data below shows the results of a survey to find the preferred length of work skirts for women
    aged 20-25 years.

Skirt Length	Mini	Above Knee	Below Knee	Long
Number of Women	12	38	35	15

a) Draw a chart or graph to illustrate this data.

b) If you had to report back to a client, who is looking to produce a new range of work wear for women
of this age group, what recommendations would you make based on this research?

1. a) There are three types of specification used when a product is developed. What are they?

i)

ii)

iii)

b) i) What is a Design Specification?

ii) What is a Product Specification?

2. a) Below is a list of criteria highlighted in a design brief for a waterproof coat for female hikers. Organise them into two groups, according to which you think are ESSENTIAL criteria and which you think are DESIRABLE criteria.

ESSENTIAL		DESIRABLE
	Waterproof	
	Bright colour	
	Lightweight	
	Futuristic design	
	Hood	
	Flattering shape	

b) Choose one criteria from each column and explain how you decided that one was essential and the other was desirable.

3. There are six different profiles you need to look at when finalising a design specification. What are they?

i) _____ ii) _____

iii) _____ iv) _____

v) _____ vi) _____

4. Choose one of the products below and make a list of at least six bullet points that might appear on its final design specification.

i) a child's sun hat ii) a chef's apron iii) a ski jacket

PRODUCT: _____

DESIGN SPECIFICATION:

5. a) In the textiles industry, what factors does a fabric specification take into consideration?

b) What factors does a component specification take into consideration?

6. Why do you think it is important for a commercial designer to think about aftercare and maintenance at this stage?

1. a) A client asks you to design a range of women's accessories using colours, shapes, patterns and textures linked with safari animals.

i) What animals could you use as sources of inspiration?

ii) What colours could you use in your designs?

iii) What patterns could you use?

iv) What textures could you use?

b) The client asks to see some of your design ideas. In the spaces below, use pencil sketches to show two initial ideas for one particular product eg. a hat, bag, belt.

c) What methods of surface decoration might you explore for these designs?

The following questions refer to the sketches you made on the previous page.

1. What type of data can you use to help you work out the size and proportions of your product?

2. Make a list of the properties and qualities you would look for when exploring different fabrics. Remember to pay attention to function and aesthetics.

3. Give three advantages of creating a model of your product.

i)

ii)

iii)

4. How could you use ICT to help you explore all your ideas for this brief?

5. When you evaluate your ideas and decide which ones to develop further, you need to refer back to four things. What are they?

i)   ii)

iii)   iv)

6. In the textiles industry, a designer will display their ideas in different ways depending on whether they are presenting them to a client or the production team. Why do you think this is?

1. a) Why is it a good idea to use a sketchbook throughout the course?

b) Unscramble the letters to find four items you might include in your sketchbook.

i) TONES

ii) SINGWARD

iii) SADIE

iv) SEWCHATS

c) Name four other items you might put in your sketchbook.

i)

ii)

iii)

iv)

d) How can you use your sketchbook to help you with your coursework?

e) Suggest how you can make cross-referencing between your sketchbook and coursework easier.

2. a) What is the purpose of a mood board?

b) A mood board can be used in many ways. Name four.

i)

ii)

iii)

iv)

1. You are given an open brief to design a range of textiles products to decorate a dinner table for a special occasion.

a) Choose a special occasion.

b) Collect a few images that you might include on a mood board for these products and attach them below.

2. a) What is the main difference between a trend board and a mood board?

b) What information would you expect to find in a trend book?

c) List three things a commercial designer might do when developing a product range that will be in the shops in a year's time.

i)

ii)

iii)

1. a) At which two stages of your coursework do you need to evaluate and analyse your design ideas?

i)

ii)

b) Why do you think it is important to evaluate and analyse your initial ideas before proceeding further with your work?

2. You need to ensure that your design ideas match the design brief and specification. Name four other factors you should consider at this stage.

i)

ii)

iii)

iv)

3. You produce a number of design ideas in response to a design brief. However, when you evaluate your ideas you find that your favourite design does not match the design specification. What can you do?

4. It can be very useful to ask other people for their opinions. Think of three questions you could ask them to help you evaluate your initial design ideas. Here's an example to get you started.

Do you dislike any features of this design? Explain why.

i)

ii)

iii)

1. Why do you need to develop your initial ideas?

2. a) Fill in the boxes to complete this diagram showing the four main stages of development.

Stage 1	Stage 2	Stage 3	Stage 4
			Final images

b) How will drawings made at Stage 2 differ from those made at Stage 1?

c) What supporting material should accompany your Stage 3 designs?

3. Look at the design for a T-shirt shown below. Draw the T-shirt in the space alongside making three modifications to the design. Clearly label the changes you have made.

ORIGINAL DESIGN

Front view

yellow sleeves

seam

red body

blue trimming

MODIFIED DESIGN

1. a) What is 'ergonomics'?

b) Why should designers be concerned with ergonomics?

2. What is 'anthropometrics'?

3. A designer might argue that using ergonomic and anthropometric data in the design process will take longer and cost more money. How would you respond to this?

4. If you were designing a hat, you would need to use anthropometric data for the average circumference of a person's head in your target group.

a) Name six other textiles products for which you would need to use anthropometric data.

i)   ii)

iii)   iv)

v)   vi)

b) Choose one of your answers from part a) and make a list of all the anthropometric data (i.e. different measurements) you would need to look at during the design process.

PRODUCT:

DATA NEEDED:

1. What three factors can affect the properties of a fabric?

i) _____   ii) _____

iii) _____

2. Give two properties that you would look for when choosing a suitable fabric for each of these products.

a) A 'throw' cover for an armchair

i) _____

ii) _____

b) A child's soft toy

i) _____

ii) _____

c) A paramedics uniform

i) _____

ii) _____

3. Briefly describe how you can manipulate wool by felting it.

4. What techniques can be used to give fabric a 3D appearance?

5. You can recycle materials to create a new product e.g. make a bag from a pair of old jeans and a belt. Come up with two new ideas for textiles products made from recycled materials and describe them below. Include a sketch for each.

IDEA 1	IDEA 2

1. Complete this crossword about different methods of using colour and surface decoration.

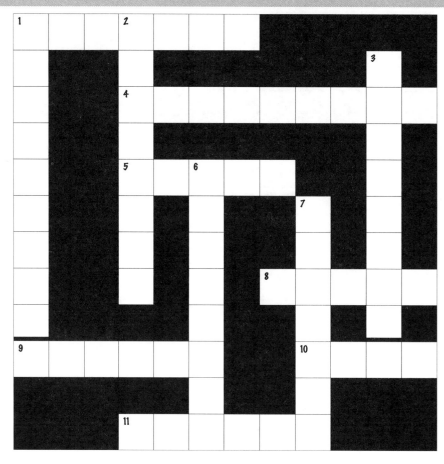

ACROSS
1. Surface decoration can _____ the appearance of fabrics. (7)
4. A method which combines small pieces of different fabrics. (9)
5. The country where Shisha work originates. (5)
8. In the first stage of 3 Down, designs are made on this. (5)
9. Printing is one method of applying this. (6)
10. A source of heat sometimes used in 3 Down. (4)
11. Another popular method of adding 9 Across. (6)

DOWN
1. Beads, buttons and shells can all be used to _____ fabrics. (9)
2. Rachel Howard specialises in this technique. (8)
3. A method of printing only suitable for fabrics with at least 50% synthetic content. (8)
6. The type of dye used in 3 Down. (8)
7. A form of embellishment. (7)

2. How are computers used in transfer printing?

3. Where might textiles manufacturers showcase new techniques?

1. a) What is a toile?

b) Why might it be necessary to make several toiles for one product?

2. Give three good reasons for creating a toile.

i)

ii)

iii)

3. There are several easy methods of creating a toile, rather than starting from scratch. Name two.

i)

ii)

4. Decide which of these statements are true and which are false.

i) Creating a toile allows you to estimate how much fabric will be needed for the actual product.   TRUE/FALSE

ii) Toiles should be made from the same fabric as the final product.   TRUE/FALSE

iii) Toile is the French word for 'dummy'.   TRUE/FALSE

iv) In the textiles industry, toiles are an essential part of the design process.   TRUE/FALSE

v) The production of a toile can help to work out the most efficient way to make a product.   TRUE/FALSE

vi) In 'haute couture' the term toile is only ever applied to prototype garments which are made into a product.   TRUE/FALSE

1. Give two reasons for using ICT to develop your designs.

i)

ii)

2. Explain in detail how you might use the following in your coursework.

i) Digital Camera:

ii) Spreadsheets:

iii) Image Mapping:

iv) Pattern Drafting Software:

v) CAD/Graphics Software:

vi) Scanner:

3. Name one software application in which you can create spreadsheets.

4. What does the term 'colourways' mean?

©Lonsdale Revision Guide Reference: Page 57

1. a) Why is it important to test and evaluate your product throughout the design process?

b) Why is it important to test and evaluate your product at the end of the production process?

2. Product tests can be split into two areas. Complete the diagram to show what they are.

TESTING

3. Describe how you can test if the materials you have chosen for your product are suitable for your target market.

4. Choose one item of clothing that you are wearing.

a) Sketch the garment in the box below and include a brief description, including the material(s) it is made from and any components used.

SKETCH	DESCRIPTION

b) Make a list of quality checks that the manufacturer might have carried out on this garment.

1. Choose one of the products below. Name two different properties you would need to test fabrics for to assess their suitability for the product. Describe how you would test for each of these properties and include a diagram.

    i) Jogging pants   ii) A child's pyjamas   iii) Tea towel

    PRODUCT: ....

    > TEST 1: ....

    > TEST 2: ....

2. a) Devise your own experiment for testing a fabric's durability to washing. Make a list of all the equipment you would need and write clear instructions for how to conduct the test.

EQUIPMENT	INSTRUCTIONS

    b) How would you record the results for your test?

    ....
    ....

1. What is the main purpose of imposing regulations and legislation on products?

2. What methods can designers use to protect their ideas?

3. Which organisation devises and regulates the tests for consumer products?

4. For each pair of sentences, underline the one that is most accurate.

a) i) Every component of a textile product must be tested under BSi guidelines

   ii) Only the finished product needs to be tested under BSi guidelines

b) i) Tests are carried out at the end of the production process

   ii) Tests are carried out at every stage of the production process

c) i) The tests are standard, so all manufacturers test their products in the same way

   ii) Manufacturers can devise their own methods of testing

d) i) The tests are not compulsory but they make your product more saleable

   ii) All consumer products must pass the relevant BSi tests

5. a) What is this symbol called?

b) If you buy a product and it has this symbol on the label, what does it mean?

6. Name three regulations relevant to ALL textiles products.

i)

ii)

iii)

1. What is the main purpose of labelling products?

2. List six types of information you would expect to find on a label for a textiles product?

   i) .... ii) ....

   iii) .... iv) ....

   v) .... vi) ....

3. Place a tick by the label that shows the correct way in which information about fibre content should be presented.

   a)
   | 2% Elastane |
   | 17% Nylon |
   | 81% Viscose |

   b)
   | 81% Viscose |
   | 17% Nylon |
   | 2% Lycra® |

   c)
   | 81% Viscose |
   | 17% Nylon |
   | 2% Elastane |

4. Special symbols are often used to show that a product is made from pure fibre. If a product had this symbol on its label, what would the fibre content be?

5. You are asked to label a garment for retail sale. Use the diagram below to show where you would attach the labels. In each instance, state the type of label you would use and the kind of information it would have on it.

Hand washing	Machine washing	Dry cleaning	Ironing or pressing
	40	(P)	

1. Look at care labels on textiles products around you. Find two more symbols used and draw them in the boxes below. Include a short description of what they mean.

i)

ii)

2. Design a care label, using symbols, following the guidelines given below.

i) Machine washable at 40°C

ii) Do not tumble dry

iii) Do not bleach

iv) Use a cool iron

v) Can be dry cleaned

3. There are four principle regulations that apply to textiles products. What are they?

i)

ii)

iii)

iv)

4. What two types of textiles products are subject to especially strict labelling rules regarding flammability?

i)

ii)

1. At what stage is it appropriate to put together a product specification?

a) At the beginning of the design process before you do anything else.

b) After production is complete.

c) After the design work is completed and before samples are made up.

ANSWER:

2. What is the purpose of a product specification?

a) To establish the essential and desirable criteria for a product.

b) To provide detailed guidelines for making a prototype and to help finalise costings.

c) To provide comprehensive instructions for manufacturing the final product.

ANSWER:

3. A product specification...

a) ... needs to be detailed, accurate and clear.

b) ... is a set of simple bullet points.

c) ... only needs to provide a rough outline.

ANSWER:

4. It is a good idea to present your product specification on a single sheet. In the box below plan the layout for a product specification, clearly showing where you would place each piece of essential information.

1.   a) What is a 'pattern'?

b) What usually provides the starting point for creating a pattern?

2.   a) There are four different ways of producing a pattern. What are they?

i)   ii)

iii)   iv)

b) Choose the method that you are most likely to use in your coursework and describe how you create a pattern that way.

.   If you have access to pattern generation software, why might this be the best option to choose?

.   Give six reasons why you might find your pattern needs adapting after making a toile.

i)   ii)

iii)   iv)

v)   vi)

.   If you found that the pattern was too big, how might you make the appropriate changes?

1. In the squared paper provided, produce a Gantt chart using the information below:

Lay out fabric	3 mins
Cut fabric	9 mins
Check cutting accuracy	2 mins
Sew side seams	3 mins
Sew arm seams	3 mins
Sew on arms	4 mins
Check sewing accuracy	2 mins
Packaging	5 mins

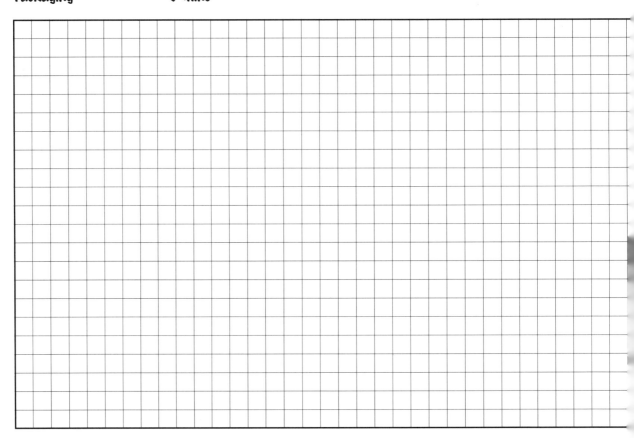

2. In the space below outline the key issues you would include in your manufacturing specification.

. In the space below, draw a flow chart to represent the information provided for the Gantt chart on the previous page

. This control system flow chart for making swimming shorts has become mixed up. Rearrange it and add arrows so that it makes sense and indicate where feedback systems could be built in.

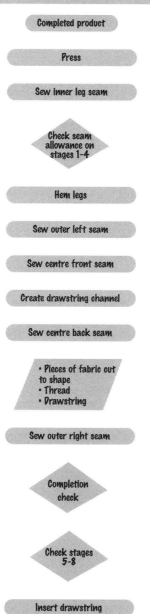

Completed product

Press

Sew inner leg seam

Check seam allowance on stages 1-4

Hem legs

Sew outer left seam

Sew centre front seam

Create drawstring channel

Sew centre back seam

• Pieces of fabric cut to shape
• Thread
• Drawstring

Sew outer right seam

Completion check

Check stages 5-8

Insert drawstring

1. For each of the statements below, write two lines explaining how they might apply when it comes to making your final product for your coursework.

   a) Follow your manufacturing specification.

   b) Use equipment safely.

   c) Make use of CAM.

   d) Ensure that you check Quality Assurance.

   e) Cost the final product.

   f) Evaluate your product.

2. List in the spaces below six key skills or techniques you used in your project.

   i)

   ii)

   iii)

   iv)

   v)

   vi)

1. The pictures show the front and back of a pair of jeans.

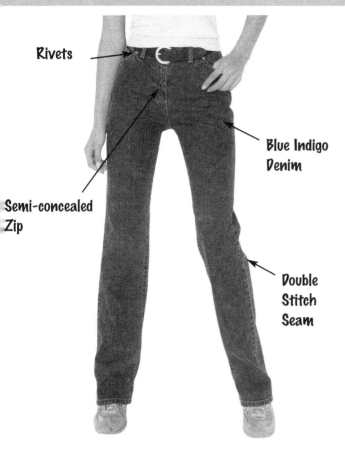

Rivets

Semi-concealed Zip

Blue Indigo Denim

Double Stitch Seam

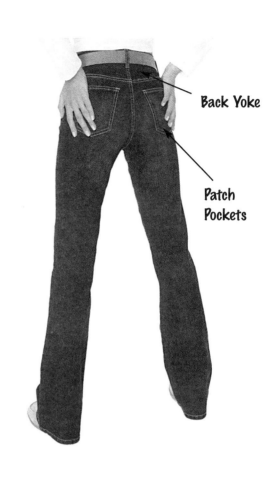

Back Yoke

Patch Pockets

a) Why have rivets been used on the pockets?

b) Suggest an alternative fabric instead of denim and give reasons for your choice.

c) Give two advantages for using a double stitched seam.

i)

ii)

d) What is the purpose of the yoke?

e) How could you use CAD/CAM to add a decorative feature?

1. What are the advantages of using computers? Tick the correct options.

They can be very expensive to buy and install. ☐	They reduce the amount of time needed to create a product. ☐	They improve communication. ☐
Software goes out of date and needs upgrading / replacing frequently. ☐	They reduce repetitive work. ☐	
Long periods of use can damage eyesight. ☐	They improve efficiency and therefore decrease production costs. ☐	

2. For each of the abbreviations below, state what it stands for and give a brief description of what it means.

a) CAM

b) CIM

3. Computers have led to the development of lots of new methods of communication. For each example below, suggest one way in which it could be used by the textile or fashion industry.

a) Video conferencing

b) Social network sites (e.g. My Space or You Tube)

4. Digital cameras represent one area of technology that is rapidly advancing. Suggest one way in which a digital camera could be used by the textile or fashion industry at each of the following stages of product development.

a) Research

b) Design

1. The sequence of the Pre-production phase shown below has become mixed up. Rearrange the stages into their correct order and write them in the space below.

A Present ideas using presentation mood boards developed using specialised graphics packages.

B Design fabric range using specialised CAD graphics software.

C Research design ideas using on-line research.

D Drape fabric on product using either 2D mapping or 3D Image Draping system.

E Fit/construction and garment specification created.

F Create and develop initial design range using vector drawing graphics software.

1st	2nd	3rd	4th	5th	6th

2. Rearrange these stages of the Production phase into the correct order.

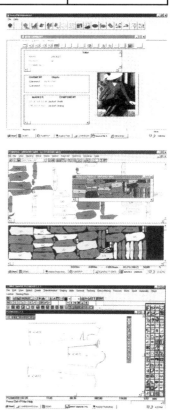

A Using PDM software (Product Data Management) and Manufacturing Specifications, costings are generated. PDM systems enable tracking of all the materials and components for the product before manufacture starts.

B Testing department does product testing for all relevant parts of the product. 3D image can also be generated via a flat 2D pattern and mapped on a computer model called an 'Avatar'.

C Product sent to production line (all details sent to manufacturing plant which can be abroad). Product is made.

D Fabrics are cut out using a specialised cutting table. Production sample is made.

E A computerised lay plan is created which calculates the best way of laying all the pattern pieces on the fabrics so that there is very little wastage.

F Product Specification sent to Pattern Making who will create pattern using pattern generation software.

1st	2nd	3rd	4th	5th	6th

3. Describe how ICT may be used in the post-production phase.

1. List the factors which would need to be taken into account when choosing a production system.

i)

ii)

iii)

iv)

2. List the four main types of production system.

i)   ii)

iii)   iv)

3. a) Some parts of a product can be made on a sub-assembly line. Describe briefly what this is.

b) Describe one advantage of using a sub-assembly line to produce parts of a product.

4. a) What type of production would you choose to manufacture simple, red and white Santa hats at Christmas. Explain your answer.

b) What advantages are there for the workforce in using cell production?

5. a) Explain what is meant by 'just-in-time' production.

b) What disadvantage does it have?

Revision Guide Reference: Page

1. In commercial textile manufacturing, what are the advantages of having an on-site storage facility where all the materials needed for a product can be kept?

2. Why do most factories have an Inspection Area at the end of the production line?

3. a) Two types of checks are made throughout the production process. What are they?

A: _____ B: _____

b) Indicate which of these checks you would expect to be carried out in each of the following areas of a factory, by answering A or B.

i) Packing Area

ii) Overlocking Area

iii) Splitting and Sorting Area

iv) Finishing Area

4. A company are going to start manufacturing a new product. Help them put together a production plan by filling in the table below. Use the product analysis you completed on page 29 of this workbook as a starting point.

Product:	
Fabric(s):	
Components:	
Sewing Equipment Needed:	
Cutting Equipment Needed:	
Additional Equipment Needed:	
Making Up Sequence:	
Finishing Equipment Needed:	
Finishing Sequence:	

5. Using the completed table on page 60, break down the production process into separate tasks. Draw a flow chart/diagram in the space below, showing the movement of the product down the production line, from the fabric storage area to the inspection area.

1. **a)** In flow diagrams, what do 'inputs' normally consist of?

b) In flow diagrams, what do 'transformation processes' normally consist of?

c) In flow diagrams, what do 'outputs' normally consist of?

2. The stages of the control system flow chart are all mixed up randomly. Lay them out correctly in the space below including arrows and show possible feedback mechanisms.

Check cutting accuracy

Packaging

Sew side seams

Sew arm seams

Sew on arms

- Design
- Pieces of fabric
- Thread

Lay out fabric

Finished product

Cut fabric

Check sewing accuracy

Pressing

Completion check

1.   Describe briefly what factors affect the 'quality' of a product.

2.   a) Very carefully explain the meaning of the term 'quality assurance'.

b) Very carefully explain the meaning of the term 'quality control'.

3.   The diagram below shows factory guidelines for the positioning of a breast pocket on a man's shirt. The table shows the corresponding measurements for six shirts coming off the production line. Use a tick or cross to indicate whether each shirt would pass a quality control test, if the specified tolerance is +/- 3mm..

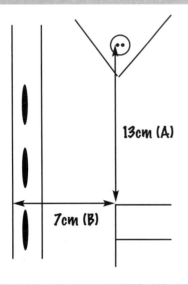

13cm (A)

7cm (B)

SHIRT	MEASUREMENT A	MEASUREMENT B	PASS?
a	13.1cm	7.2cm	
b	12.8cm	7.1cm	
c	13.2cm	6.6cm	
d	12.9cm	6.8cm	
e	13.4cm	7.0cm	
f	12.6cm	7.6cm	

4.   a) Where are spot checks usually carried out?

b) What is the purpose of spot checks?

1.   a) Who would normally carry out a risk assessment?

b) Write down six safety procedures which may be put into place as a result of the risk assessment.

i)

ii)

iii)

iv)

v)

vi)

2.   a) Explain what the following safety symbols mean:

i)

ii)

iii)

b) Explain what is meant by ISO 9000.

List five key health and safety guidelines which you should follow in order to work safely during your project.

i)

ii)

iii)

iv)

v)

1. In a visit to the factory, the Health and Safety officer noticed several problems. Explain the dangers associated with each problem and the action you would take to ensure safety.

a) The sewing machine engineers were attempting to repair machines without switching them off.

i) This is dangerous because...

ii) It could be made safe by...

b) In the pressing room, the steam function is left permanently on.

i) This is dangerous because...

ii) It could be made safe by...

c) The sewing machine operators were eating their lunch at their work station.

i) This is dangerous because...

ii) It could be made safe by...

d) Sharp cutting equipment was left lying around the work area.

i) This is dangerous because...

ii) It could be made safe by...

2. List six factors which must be taken into account when designing and making products for children.

i)   iv)

ii)   v)

iii)   vi)

1. List seven different ways in which you could advertise a new product.

i)	
ii)	
iii)	
iv)	
v)	
vi)	
vii)	

Alongside your choices, in the columns provided, number them 1-7 in order of how effective you think they would be, and then label them A-G in order of how expensive they might be.

2. What can you deduce from this about the effectiveness of advertising and its costs?

3. How might a product be 'pushed' within the retail outlet itself? Try to outline 4 ways.

4. How are the general public protected from misleading or event fraudulent advertising?

When marketing a product it can be distributed through several outlets. List 6 possible outlets.

i)	iv)
ii)	v)
iii)	vi)

1. a) What does primary packaging consist of?

b) What does secondary packaging consist of?

2. The textile product you have designed is a silk shirt. Describe the packaging that you would use to contain this product under the following headings:

a) How will the customer know what it is?

b) Where would the size be displayed?

c) How would the product be protected by the packaging?

d) What type of secondary packaging would be used during transport?

e) How could you make sure that the packaging materials could be recycled?

3. What is meant by the term 'over packaging'?

What is the primary reason for wearing clothing?

When holidaying abroad, why is it important to find out about the culture beforehand and pack appropriate clothing?

Name one social group that can be easily identified by their clothing, and describe how they dress.

The manufacture of everyday products can impact on the environment and on the lives of other people.

a) Briefly describe one way in which the manufacture of a product can impact on the environment.

b) Briefly describe one way in which the manufacture of a product can impact on the lives of other people.

What is meant by the term Ethical Trading?

a) What does IFAT stand for?

b) List four standards that are enforced by IFAT to ensure their members trade fairly and ethically.

i)

ii)

iii)

1. What is meant by the term 'From the Cradle to the Grave'?

2. What is purpose of analysing a product's lifecycle from the cradle to the grave?

3. The lifecycle of a cotton shirt begins with the cotton farmer. Cotton comes from a plant, which is harvested using heavy machinery.

   a) Cotton farming uses energy. Suggest one way in which this energy might be used.

   b) Cotton farming produces waste products. Suggest one waste product that might be produced.

   c) Cotton farmers often use pesticides to get rid of insects that could damage the crop. This has a negativ effect on wildlife and bird populations in the area. Why do you think that is?

   d) Cotton can be grown organically, however, most manufacturers still choose to buy cotton that has bee intensively farmed using chemicals like pesticides. Why do you think that is?

   e) Suggest two other stages in the lifecycle of a cotton shirt which require a high energy input.

      i)

      ii)

   f) Suggest two other stages in the lifecycle of a cotton shirt which produce waste.

      i)

      ii)

   g) Suggest an environmentally friendly alternative to disposing of the cotton shirt in a landfill site at the end of its lifecycle.

1. Because of the machinery and processes involved, a lot of energy is used in the manufacture of a textiles product. However, a large amount of energy is still consumed after the product is bought by a consumer.

a) What is energy needed for at this stage of the product's lifecycle?

b) Suggest three ways in which energy consumption at this stage of the lifecycle could be reduced.

i)

ii)

iii)

2. The fashion industry promotes new lines every season, encouraging consumers to buy new clothes and update their wardrobe.

a) Name two ways in which this produces textile waste.

i)

ii)

b) Suggest three ways in which energy consumption at this stage of the lifecycle could be reduced.

i)

ii)

iii)

Make a checklist of points to think about at the design and development stage of a new product, to ensure that it is as environmentally friendly as possible. You can refer back to this checklist throughout the course.

1. **a) What is meant by 'recycling'?**

b) Describe what you understand by Primary Recycling.

c) Describe what you understand by Secondary or Physical Recycling.

d) Describe what you understand by Tertiary or Chemical Recycling.

2. **List three key reasons for recycling.**

i)

ii)

iii)

3. **In the space below sketch your ideas for a poster encouraging people to recycle.**

©*Lonsdale* **Revision Guide Reference: Page**